Student Workbook

Contents

D1383277

Process Control Modes

Using Your Training Program

This is a comprehensive videotape/text training program. It may be used for independent self-study, or in a traditional classroom setting.

The videotapes are divided into segments, varying in length from four to six minutes.

This workbook is also divided into segments that generally correspond to the videotape segments.

Throughout the workbook, you will find symbols that will help you to identify how the information is organized:

Objective
Goal

Application
Doing
Hands-On

Self-Check
Review Questions
Pre/Post Test

Bibliography
Reference/Standard

**Calculator
Exercises
Computation**

**Concept/Idea
Understanding
Theory**

**Closer Look
More Information**

You may alternately view a segment of videotape and read the corresponding segment in your workbook. A variety of questions and practical exercises are provided to further your understanding of the subject.

If you are undertaking your training in a classroom setting, your instructor will administer a pretest and a post test during the course. Final evaluation of your progress through the training program will be based on a combination of test scores and observation of your performance during hands-on exercises.

Student Workbook

Overview

The *Process Control Modes* training program describes the function of controllers in instrument control systems and explains the four modes of control action commonly used to control industrial process operations. The types of control modes covered in this program are two-position control, proportional control, integral control, and derivative control. At the end of your study of *Process Control Modes*, you should be able to perform the training objectives of this program.

Prerequisites

An understanding of the fundamental principles that apply to all control systems may be helpful to persons beginning their study of process control systems. These principles are explained in the ITTP/2 program entitled *Feedback Control*.

Program Objectives

Two-Position Control

1. Describe the function of a controller in a process loop.
2. Identify the four modes of control.
3. Describe the operating principle of two-position control.
4. Describe the effect of two-position control in a process loop.

Proportional Control

5. Describe the function of continuous control.
6. Describe the operating principle of proportional control.
7. Define proportional band.
8. Describe the effects of changing the width of a proportional band.

PID Control

9. Explain the importance of having the proper amount of proportional control.
10. Define the term *offset*.
11. Describe the function of integral control.
12. Describe the function of derivative control.

Segment 1

Process industries provide countless types of goods and services. Just as the types of goods and services vary, the control methods used in production vary. Some processes require very little control; that is, they can operate successfully with a wide range of tolerance. Others may require much finer control. The specific process determines the type of control required. The component in the loop that provides automatic process control is the controller.

Define the function of a controller in a process loop.

A control loop is designed to respond to upsets in the process. Upsets are external conditions that change the demand placed on the control system and cause changes in the process variables. The controller makes the decisions that affect the variables in the process, so the role of the controller is critical.

The devices in a typical process loop include a sensor, transmitter, controller, and a final control element. The sensor measures the value of the controlled variable. This value is converted to a standard instrument signal by a transmitter. The transmitter sends the signal to the controller. The controller compares the signal to a set point and, based on any deviation, decides what, if any, action is required. The controller's output signal positions the final control element. The final control element responds to the output signal by changing the value of the manipulated variable. The manipulated variable, in turn, affects the value of the controlled variable, which is again detected by the sensor. This action continues until the value of the controlled variable matches the set point. The action of algorithms within the controller are combined to produce the desired control action. These algorithms are usually referred to as control modes.

Identify the four modes of control.

There are four control modes: two-position control, proportional control, integral control, and derivative control. Two-position control is the simplest mode of control. With two-position control, the signal to the final control element is either zero percent or 100 percent. Proportional, integral, and derivative control modes are continuous. A controller may be equipped with one or more continuous control modes.

Two-Position Control

Describe the operating principle of two-position control.

A home heating system is an example of two-position control. The heating system turns on when the room temperature falls below the set point. When the temperature in the room exceeds the set point, the heating system turns off.

In process systems that do not require precise control, two-position, or on/off control, may be adequate. Typical industrial two-position control operates on the principles illustrated in the following process diagram. The liquid stored in the tank must be maintained close to a specific temperature, so temperature is the controlled variable in this example. Steam is the manipulated variable.

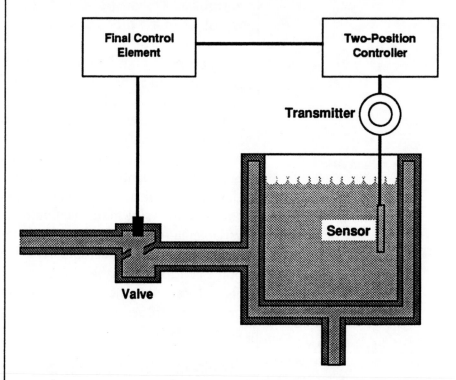

The components in this loop include a sensor, a transmitter, a two-position controller, and a final control element, which, in this case, is a valve. With two-position control, the valve has only two positions: open or closed. Changes in product temperature are detected by the sensor and signals representing any changes are transmitted to the controller. The controller determines that the temperature is below set point and sends a signal to open the steam valve. The valve opens, increasing steam flow, which is the manipulated variable, to heat the tank.

Two-Position Control

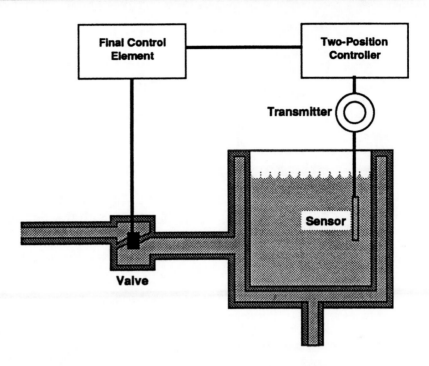

Feedback is continuous, so the sensor continuously measures the temperature of the liquid and converts this information to signals that are transmitted to the controller. When the steam flow to the tank is initiated, the temperature will return to the set point value. The temperature will continue to rise, however, until further action is taken. When the temperature of the liquid exceeds set point, a signal to close the valve is sent to the final control element.

Describe the effect of two-position control in a process loop.

It should be noted that the control loop cannot respond immediately to changes. Two factors prohibit immediate response: the response time of the sensor and the time required for the liquid in the tank to respond to changes in the manipulated variable. In this example, temperature changes are delayed by the time required for the steam to heat the liquid or, having heated the liquid to a temperature above set point, for the liquid to cool to the point at which it matches the set point. Consequently, two-position control can cause significant oscillations in the process. If the process can tolerate the oscillations in the controlled variable, two-position control is adequate. If the process cannot tolerate oscillations, a different control method must be used.

Two-Position Control

Hands-On Exercises

1. Identify processes in your facility in which two-position control is used.

2. Locate examples of controllers in your facility that provide various combinations of continuous control.

Review Questions

1. The following paragraph describes a typical control loop. Fill in the blanks with the appropriate terms.

   A change in the value of the controlled variable is caused by an _____. Information on this change is detected by the _____. The change in value is sent as a signal from the _____ to the _____, where it is compared to a _____. Based on the deviation, an output signal is sent to the _____, which changes the value of the _____.

2. List the four modes of control.
   a. _____
   b. _____
   c. _____
   d. _____

3. Of the four control modes, the only mode that is not continuous is _____.

4. Two-position control is not appropriate for all processes because it causes _____ in the controlled variable.

Segment 2

For many processes, a control loop in which the final control element has only two positions does not provide adequate control. Two-position control can cause significant oscillations that the process cannot tolerate. The alternative is a continuous control mode, such as proportional control, integral control, derivative control, or a combination of these continuous control modes.

Describe the function of continuous control.

Continuous control positions the final control element in more than two positions. Essentially, this means the final control element can be positioned at any point within its throttling range, not just on or off. Oscillations in the process are minimized because a finer degree of control is possible.

Describe the operating principle of proportional control.

Proportional control is often used in process systems where the value of the controlled variable is constantly changing in response to upsets. The operating principle of proportional control can be illustrated by considering how pressure can be controlled in a boiler. The steam produced is the controlled variable. The flow rate of the fuel is the manipulated variable.

The dynamics of the process prohibit the use of a two-position control mode. Two-position control cannot keep the boiler pressure within tolerable limits. The on/off action of the valve would cause pressure to fluctuate because either too much or no fuel would be available to the burner.

Proportional control action can provide much smoother control and reduce oscillations. When the proportional controller receives the signal from the sensor, which is the pressure transmitter on the steam header, the controller responds to any deviation from set point by positioning the final control element. The final control element, a fuel control valve, can be in the open position, the closed position, or at any position in between. So, it will be positioned in proportion to the deviation. The ability to adjust the position of the valve allows for a more gradual adjustment of fuel flow as the pressure in the boiler changes.

Proportional controllers are designed to maintain a continuous relationship between the controlled variable and the position of the final control element. For example, if the set point of the outlet pressure is 900 psi, the controller will move the fuel control valve to a position that will help to achieve that pressure. Further, the valve will be continuously repositioned to maintain the desired pressure.

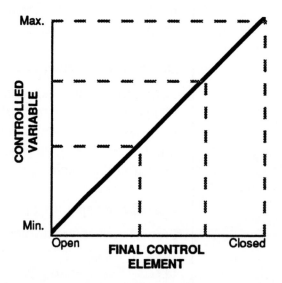

The relationship between the value of the controlled variable and the position of the final control element can be depicted graphically. When boiler pressure, the controlled variable, is at set point, less fuel is required and the valve is partially closed. Likewise, when pressure is below set point, more fuel is required and the valve is more fully open. This relationship can also be stated in different terms: a full range of input is required to produce a full range of valve movement. Any other changes in pressure cause the proportional controller to readjust the position of the fuel control valve proportionally.

Note that in the boiler pressure control loop, an increase in the controlled variable causes the final control element to close. It should be understood that the relationship between the controller's output signal and the resulting motion of the final control element can be achieved in one of two ways: through the use of a reverse-acting controller or through the use of a direct-acting controller.

For example, a reverse-acting controller would respond to an increase in the value of the process variable by decreasing its output signal to the fuel control valve. A direct-acting controller would respond to an increase in the value of the controlled variable by increasing its output signal to the control valve.

Proportional Control

Process systems vary widely in design. In the steam boiler application, the controller responded to increases in the controlled variable, boiler pressure, by signaling the final element to close. Other applications may be better served by an arrangement in which an increase in the controlled variable requires the final control element to open.

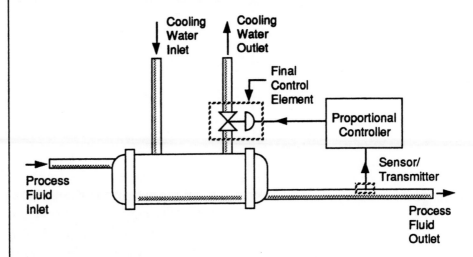

For example, in this system, a shell and tube heat exchanger is used to cool a process fluid to the set point temperature. A sensor monitors the process fluid outlet temperature and sends a signal to the transmitter. The transmitter relays the temperature signal to the controller. The controller compares the transmitter's output signal to set point and decides what, if any, corrective action is required. The controller then sends a signal to the final control element to position the valve so that the process fluid outlet temperature will return to set point.

Assume then that the process fluid outlet temperature increases. As the temperature increases, the controller and the cooling water outlet valve work together to allow more cooling water flow through the heat exchanger. Here also, the relationship between the controller input signal and the resulting motion of the final control element is determined by the controller action.

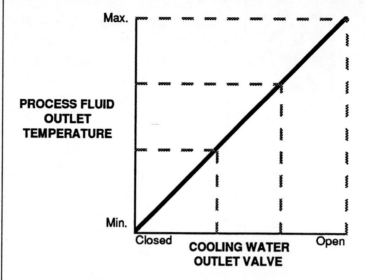

PROCESS FLUID
OUTLET
TEMPERATURE

COOLING WATER
OUTLET VALVE

In this example, the controller is direct-acting. In response to an increase in the value of the process variable, the controller produces an increase in output. The cooling water control valve responds to the higher controller output signal by opening to allow more cooling water flow through the heat exchanger. If a reverse-acting controller were used, its output signal would decrease as process fluid outlet temperature increased.

Define the term proportional band.

The term *proportional band* designates the amount of input change needed to provide a full range of output change.

In most cases, the amount of proportional control action is adjustable. This adjustment is referred to as changing the width, or percentage, of the proportional band. Proportional band is usually referred to in percentage.

Proportional band can be calculated by using this equation:

$$PB = \frac{1}{Gain} \times 100\%$$

For example, if the gain is 1.33, then the proportional band is set at 75%.

$$PB = \frac{1}{Gain} \times 100\%$$

$$PB = \frac{1}{1.33} \times 100\%$$

$$PB = 75\%$$

Changes in proportional control action are also expressed as changes in proportional gain. Proportional gain is the ratio of the change in output to the change in input.

Proportional gain can be calculated by using this equation:

$$Gain = \frac{100\%}{PB}$$

For example, if the proportional band is 75%, then gain is 1.33. Note that gain is usually expressed as a dimensionless number, unlike proportional band.

$$Gain = \frac{100\%}{75\%}$$

$$Gain = 1.33$$

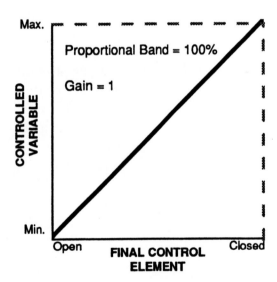

In the application used as an example, 100 percent input is required to obtain a full range of output, so the proportional band is 100 percent. Using the formula given, the gain is 1.

$$\text{Gain} = \frac{100\%}{PB}$$

$$\text{Gain} = \frac{100\%}{100\%}$$

$$\text{Gain} = 1$$

Describe the effects of changing the width of a proportional band.

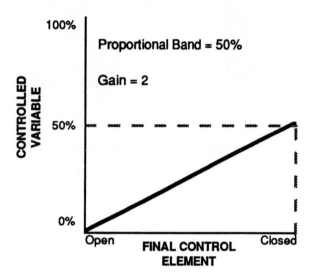

Assume the proportional action in the system has been adjusted so that only half the change in input is needed to fully open or close the valve. Then, the same output could be achieved with half as much input. Because only 50 percent input is required to obtain a full range of output, the proportional band is 50 percent and the gain is 2.

$$PB = \frac{1}{2} \times 100\%$$

$$PB = 50\%$$

$$\text{Gain} = \frac{100\%}{50\%}$$

$$\text{Gain} = 2$$

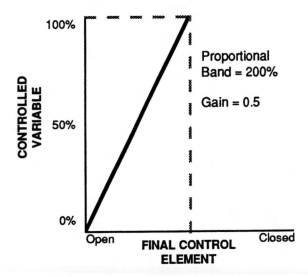

The opposite effect can be achieved by adjusting the proportional band in the opposite direction. Assume a full range of input change results in a 50 percent change in output. The result is that the same input achieves only half as much output. Therefore, the calculations are as follows:

$$PB = \frac{100\%}{50\%} \times 100\%$$

$$PB = 2 \times 100\%$$

$$PB = 200\%$$

$$Gain = \frac{50\%}{100\%}$$

$$Gain = 0.5$$

The proportional band is 200%. The gain is 0.5.

A wide proportional band or low gain corresponds to a less sensitive response. A narrow proportional band or high gain corresponds to a more sensitive response. The amount of proportional action a controller is capable of can accurately be expressed by either proportional band or gain. However, it is important to realize that proportional band and gain are inversely related, that is, as proportional band increases, gain decreases. A sound understanding of proportional action is essential when adjusting the proportional band or gain in process control loops.

Proportional Control

Determining the optimal proportional band for a process is often a process of trial and error based on careful observation over time. Chart records from a recording controller can provide the information necessary to make the decision. The factors that determine the optimal band include the nature and frequency of upsets to the system and the control characteristics of the process.

Hands-On Exercises

1. Identify the processes in your facility that cannot tolerate significant oscillations.

2. Discuss the probable impact that proportional band adjustments have on the variables that are being controlled in a specific process.

Review Questions

1. Which of the following are true of proportional control? Indicate as many answers as apply.
    a. The final control element can be positioned at any point in its throttling range.
    b. Oscillations are minimized.
    c. Proportional control is often used when the value of the controlled variable is constantly changing.
    d. Proportional control provides a finer degree of control.

2. Proportional controllers are designed so that there is a continuous relationship between which two components?
    a. The controlled variable and the controller
    b. The controlled variable and the final control element
    c. The manipulated variable and the controller
    d. The manipulated variable and the final control element

3. Proportional gain is defined as the ratio of the _____ to the _____.

4. If proportional action were adjusted so that only half the change in input would be needed to fully open or close a valve, the proportional band would be _____ and the proportional gain would be _____.

5. A wide proportional band corresponds to a (less/more) sensitive response, while a narrow proportional band corresponds to a (less/more) sensitive response.

6. If an input change from 30% to 40% results in an output change from 20% to 60%, what are the proportional band and gain?

7. Initially, a controller receives an input signal of 50% and an output signal of 60%. If the controller's gain is set at 2, what will the new output signal be when input increases to 60%?

Segment 3

It is safe to assume that no two process systems are identical. Thus, the amount of control action demanded for a system is determined by the individual process. Because every process has its own characteristics and variables, each has a specific proportional action within which maximum efficiency can be obtained. Proportional control action provides continuous control by responding directly to the magnitude of the error or deviation. A proportional control mode that does not include any other type of action, such as integral or derivative action, is a relatively simple form of control. Further, proportional control is inherently stable when the controller is properly tuned, that is, adjusted to work within the process it is controlling. It also stands to reason that a PI or PID controller is significantly more complex than a proportional only controller.

Explain the importance of having the proper amount of proportional control.

Proper control action provides quick response, but it is not so rapid that the process cycles erratically. Oscillation does occur but not excessively, and, as the oscillations settle, the process reaches a steady state.

When proportional action is excessive, small deviations from set point result in significant changes in output. Insufficient control action allows virtually no control: large changes in input cause only small changes in output. Generally, proper control action is somewhere between these two extremes.

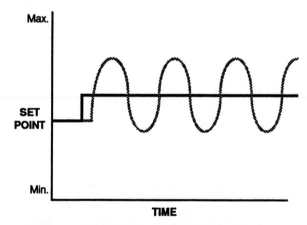

This is the effect of a proportional band that is too narrow. The relatively small change in set point results in a significant change in output, causing an oscillating effect similar to two-position control action.

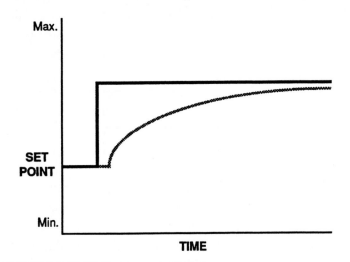

On the other hand, a proportional band that is too wide also creates difficulties. A large change in input causes very little change in output, causing control action to take place very slowly over a long period of time.

Define the term offset.

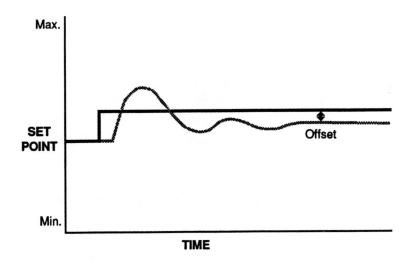

As shown in this illustration, after the process reaches a steady state, there is a difference between the set point and the value of the process variable. The term used to express the difference between the set point and the value of the process variable is *offset*.

PID Control

Offset is inherent in proportional control modes and must be corrected. Because proportional control produces corrections proportional to deviations, it stands to reason that no corrections are produced unless there is some deviation. Therefore, after any upset, some deviation will remain. The necessary or prolonged deviation associated with proportional control is offset.

The concept is easily understood if considered in terms of how the speed of a car is controlled. Assume that a car is being driven along a flat road at the speed limit, 55 miles per hour. The position of the accelerator is appropriate to maintain speed. However, the landscape changes suddenly, and the car begins to climb a hill. Without any intervention, the speed of the car will decrease. The response is to apply proportional action, that is, to depress the accelerator an amount proportional to the amount that the speed of the car decreases, or, in different terms, to apply proportional action that corresponds to the amount of error or deviation.

The effect of the action is that the speed stops decreasing and steadies out again. At this point, the car is traveling up the hill at a constant speed, but it is no longer operating at 55 miles per hour. More likely, the speed is slower; assume a speed of 50 miles per hour. Offset is the difference between the set point — 55 miles per hour — and the actual steady-state traveling speed of 50 miles per hour. At this stage, offset can only be corrected by further depressing the accelerator to provide the engine with slightly more gas, and checking the speedometer to see the effect. This sequence of adjusting and checking is repeated until the desired speed of 55 miles per hour is obtained.

Describe the function of integral control.

Industrial proportional controllers usually have a second control action designed to eliminate offset with the same sequence of steps, check, adjust, and recheck the status of the controlled variable until the process returns to set point. In other words, integral action, which is the term applied to this control mode, responds to the duration of the error. Integral action may also be referred to as reset action. Note: Integral action is often called reset because it "resets" the controller output over time until set point is reached. Reset action is determined in "repeats per minute" or "minutes per repeat." Regardless of which term is used to describe it, integral

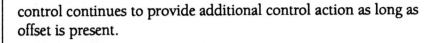

control continues to provide additional control action as long as offset is present.

Ideally, the rate at which integral or reset action is implemented does not have a negative impact on the stability of the process due to lag time. The only type of application in which lag time is almost never a problem is in flow control. Flow control loops are very fast and often noisy. Therefore, integral control action is often added to the feedback controller in flow loops to provide a dampening or filtering action for the loop. Integral action should return the process variable to set point as quickly as possible without creating significant oscillation in the system. Integral action can be adjusted in the same manner as proportional action. It should be noted that integral control cannot be used to stabilize a process. Stabilization is achieved through proportional control action. Integral action is only designed to eliminate offset.

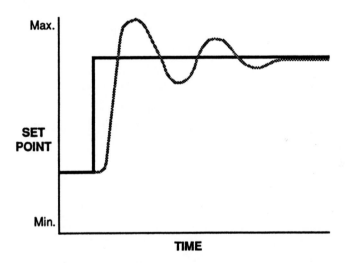

This illustration shows the effect of integral control action. Integral action provides output to the final control element until the process returns to set point. When proportional control is combined with integral control, the proportional control action is repeated until the final control element is positioned to correct offset. Proportional-plus-integral control is referred to as PI control.

Describe the function of derivative control.

Proportional and integral actions can also be combined with derivative action, or rate, to compensate for processes that have a slow response, such as a temperature control loop. Derivative action responds to how rapidly a process is deviating from set point. Proportional-plus-integral-plus-derivative, or PID, control is the most complex of the control modes.

A PID controller responds rapidly to upsets in the process; thus, there is less lag time. The term "lag" is used in this context to refer to the time-dependent nature of processes or to the behavior of components in the process control loop. When the process or component is slow to respond, the output will lag behind any input. Derivative action will compensate for these lags, and reduce oscillations and overshoot.

In order to tune PID controllers, three adjustments are required. However, once each of the actions is properly tuned, the controller can provide very precise control of the process. PID controllers are commonly found in processes where temperature is the controlled variable because the response time is relatively slow. Flow control processes rarely require derivative action because the process itself responds so quickly that any derivative action would overcompensate for the rate of change.

Again, the process of driving a car provides an easily understood application of derivative control. Assume that the car has passed the crest of the hill and begun to descend a steep grade. As speed rapidly increases, the instinctive reaction is to apply heavy pressure to the brake to stop further acceleration. In terms of automatic control, the action can be described as making a temporary correction proportional to the initial rate of change, or first derivative, in the controlled variable. As the speed decreases, the "check, adjust, recheck" sequence of actions stabilizes the speed of the car at the speed limit, or set point.

PID Control

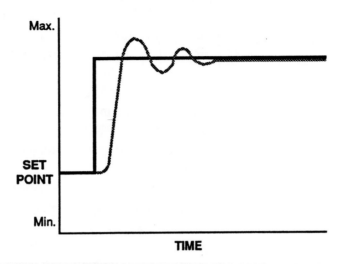

Derivative action in a process control loop is parallel to the action of rapidly switching from acceleration to deceleration, briefly overcompensating for the change in the status of the controlled variable. Derivative control tends to lead or anticipate what the next impact on the process will be, and compensate for it. As a result, this type of action effectively contributes to the stability of the process. It should be noted that derivative control is applied only until the controlled variable begins to move back toward set point. After the effect of the derivative control action is established, proportional and integral action are used to restore the value of the process variable to set point.

Derivative control is especially useful in two types of processes: those that are slow to respond and require additional control action from the controller and those in which processes are subject to frequent start-ups. In each case, derivative action produces more stability than is possible with only proportional and integral action. Derivative control enables the controller to respond more rapidly and position the final control element more quickly than is possible with only proportional and integral actions. Consequently, there is less overshoot and fewer oscillations in a control system using proportional-plus-integral-plus-derivative control. Proportional-plus-integral-plus-derivative control loops are often described as PID control.

Of the four control modes used, two-position or on/off control is the simplest control action. Two-position control responds to the presence of an error or deviation. This type of control action results in significant oscillations in the value of the controlled variable, so it is restricted to applications that do not require precise control.

Proportional control action provides more precise control. With proportional control action, a direct response to the magnitude of the error or deviation is provided. Integral, or reset, action is often combined with proportional control to correct the offset that is inherent in all proportional control. Integral action responds to the duration of the error. Derivative, or rate, action may be combined with proportional and integral action to compensate for processes that have a relatively slow response. Derivative action responds to the rate at which the process is changing from set point. Proportional, integral, and derivative control work together to provide an efficient and accurate means of automatic control.

Hands-On Exercises

1. Identify the process variables that typically require derivative action to ensure proper control.

2. Discuss the probable impact that PID adjustments have on the variables that are being controlled in a specific process.

Review Questions

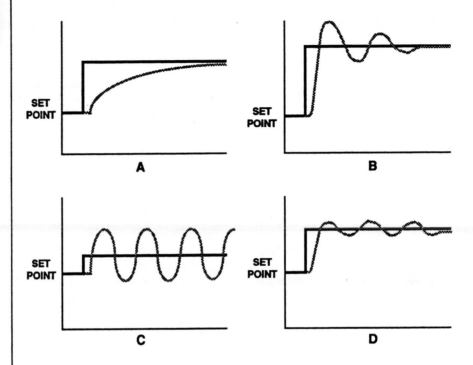

1. Which of the graphs represents excessive proportional action?

2. Which of the graphs represents insufficient proportional action?

3. Which of the graphs represents PI control?

4. Which of the following is true of the condition known as offset? Indicate as many as apply.
   a. Offset is inherent in proportional control systems.
   b. Offset is the difference between the set point and the value of the manipulated variable.
   c. Offset can be corrected by derivative control action alone.
   d. Offset can be corrected by integral control action alone.

Answer Key

Review Questions — Two-Position Control

1. The following paragraph describes a typical control loop. Fill in the blanks with the appropriate terms.

    A change in the value of the controlled variable is caused by an upset. Information on this change is detected by the sensor. The change in value is sent as a signal from the transmitter to the controller, where it is compared to a set point. Based on the deviation, an output signal is sent to the final control element, which changes the value of the manipulated variable.

2. List the four modes of control.
    a. Two-position
    b. Proportional
    c. Integral
    d. Derivative

3. Of the four control modes, the only mode that is not continuous is two-position control.

4. Two-position control is not appropriate for all processes because it causes oscillations in the controlled variable.

Review Questions — Proportional Control

1. Which of the following are true of proportional control? Indicate as many answers as apply.
    a. The final control element can be positioned at any point in its throttling range.
    b. Oscillations are minimized.
    c. Proportional control is often used when the value of the controlled variable is constantly changing.
    d. Proportional control provides a finer degree of control.

2. Proportional controllers are designed so that there is a continuous relationship between which two components?
    b. The controlled variable and the final control element

3. Proportional gain is defined as the ratio of the change in output to the change in input.

4. If proportional action were adjusted so that only half the change in input would be needed to fully open or close a valve, the proportional band would be 50% and the proportional gain would be 2.

5. A wide proportional band corresponds to a less sensitive response, while a narrow proportional band corresponds to a more sensitive response.

6. If an input change from 30% to 40% results in an output change from 20% to 60%, what is the proportional band and gain?

$$PB \quad = \quad \frac{40\% - 30\%}{60\% - 20\%} \times 100\%$$

$$= \quad \frac{10\%}{40\%} \times 100\%$$

$$= \quad 0.25 \times 100\%$$

$$= \quad 25\%$$

$$Gain \quad = \quad \frac{60\% - 20\%}{40\% - 30\%} \times 100\%$$

$$= \quad \frac{40\%}{10\%}$$

$$= \quad 4$$

7. A controller is initially at an input signal of 50% and an output signal of 60%. If the controller's gain is set at 2, what will the new output signal be when input increases to 60%?

$$Gain \quad = \quad \frac{\% \text{ of input change}}{\% \text{ of output change}}$$

(Gain) x (% change in input) = % change in output

2 x (60% - 50%) = % change in output

2 x 10% = % change in output

20% = change in output

Output = 60% + 20%

Output = 80%

Review Questions — PID Control

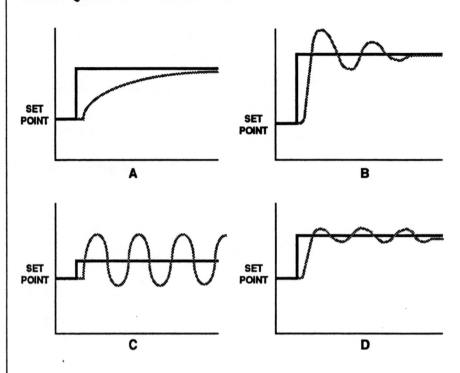

1. Which of the graphs represents excessive proportional action?
    Graph C
2. Which of the graphs represents insufficient proportional action?
    Graph A
3. Which of the graphs represents PI control? Graph B
4. Which of the following is true of the condition known as offset?
    Indicate as many as apply.
    a. Offset is inherent in proportional control systems.
    d. Offset can be corrected by integral control action alone.

Accuracy

1. The degree to which an indicated value matches the actual value of a measured variable. 2. In process instrumentation, degree of conformity of an indicated value to a recognized accepted standard value, or ideal value.

Analog signal

An analog signal is a continuously variable representation of a physical quantity, property, or condition such as pressure, flow, temperature, etc. The signal may be transmitted as pneumatic, mechanical, or electrical energy.

Cascade control

1. A control system composed of two loops where the set point of one loop (the inner loop) is controlled by the output of the second loop (the outer loop). 2. A control technique that incorporates a master and a slave loop. The master loop controls the primary control parameters and establishes the slave-loop set point. The purpose of the slave loop is to reduce the effect of disturbances on the primary control parameter and to improve the dynamic performance of the loop.

Controlled variable

1. The variable which the control system attempts to keep at the set point value. The set point may be constant or variable. 2. The part of a process you want to control (flow, level, temperature, pressure, etc.). 3. A process variable which is to be controlled at some desired value by means of manipulating another process variable.

Derivative control action

In process instrumentation, control action in which the output is proportional to the rate of change of the input.

Deviation

The difference between the value of a specific variable and some desired value, usually a process set point.

Digital signal

A discrete or discontinuous signal; often one whose various states are discrete intervals apart.

Feedback

1. Process signal used in control as a measure of response to control action. 2. The part of a closed loop system which automatically brings back information about the condition under control.

Feedback control

An error driven control system in which the control signal to the actuators is proportional to the difference between a command signal and a feedback signal from the process variable being controlled.

Feedforward control	A method of control that compensates for a disturbance before its effect is felt in the output. It is based on a model that relates the output to the input where the disturbance occurs. In distillation, the disturbances are usually feed rate and feed compositions. Steady-state feedforward models are usually combined with dynamic compensation functions to set the manipulative variables and combined with feedback adjustments (trim) to correct for control model-accuracy constraints.
Instrument	A device for measuring the value of an observable attribute; the device may merely indicate the observed value, or it may also record or control the value.
Instrumentation	Any system of instruments and associated devices used for detecting, signaling, observing, measuring, controlling, or communicating attributes of a physical object or process.
Integral control action	Control action in which the output is proportional to the time integral of the input; i.e., the rate of change of output is proportional to the input.
Manipulated variable	1. In a process that is desired to regulate some condition, a quantity or a condition that is altered by the control in order to initiate a change in the value of the regulated condition. 2. The part of the process which is adjusted to close the gap between the set point and the controlled variable.
Measured variable	1. The physical quantity, property, or condition which is to be measured. Common measured variables are temperatures, pressure, rate of flow, thickness, speed, etc. 2. The part of the process that is monitored to determine the actual condition of the controlled variable.
Offset	A constant and steady state of deviation of the measured variable from the set point.
Proportional band	The change in input required to produce a full range change in output due to proportional control action. The preferred term is proportional gain.
Proportional control	A control mode in which there is a continual linear relationship between the deviation computer in the controller, the signal of the controller, and the position of the final control element.
Proportional integral derivative (PID) control	A combination of proportional, integral, and derivative control actions.

Proportional gain — The ratio of change in output due to proportional control action to the change in input.

Precision — The degree of reproducibility among several independent measurements of the same true value.

Ratio controller — A controller that maintains a predetermined ratio between two or more variables.

Response time — 1. The time required for the absolute value of the difference between the output and its final value to become and remain less than a specified amount, following the application of a step input or disturbance. 2. The time required for the output to first reach a definite value after the application of a step input or disturbance. 3. The time it takes for a controlled variable to react to a change in input.

Set point — An input variable which sets the desired value of the controlled variable. The input variable may be manually set, automatically set or programmed. It is expressed in the same units as the controlled variable.

Two-position action — A type of control-system action that involves positioning the final control device in either of two fixed positions without permitting it to stop at any intermediate position.

Bibliography

ISA Publications

Application Concepts of Process Control. P .W. Murrill. Instrument Society of America, Research Triangle Park, NC. 1988. (ISBN: 1-55617-171-4)

Automatic Tuning of PID Controllers. K. J. Astrom and T. Hagglund. Instrument Society of America, Research Triangle Park, NC. 1988. (ISBN: 1-55617-081-5)

Electronic Controllers. L. M. Thompson. Instrument Society of America, Research Triangle Park, NC. 1989. (ISBN: 1-555617-129-3)

Fundamentals of Process Control Theory, 2nd ed. P. W. Murrill. Instrument Society of America, Research Triangle Park, NC. 1981. (ISBN: 0-87664-507-4)

Process Control Fundamentals Package. Instrument Society of America, Research Triangle Park, NC. 1987. (ISBN: 1-55617-195-1)

The Comprehensive Dictionary of Instrumentation and Control. Instrument Society of America, Research Triangle Park, NC. (ISBN: 1-55617-125-0)

Standards and Recommended Practices

ANSI/ISA-S5.1, *Instrumentation Symbols and Identification.* Instrument Society of America, Research Triangle Park, NC. 1984. (ISBN: 0-87664-844-8)

ANSI/ISA-S5.4, *Instrument Loop Diagrams.* Instrument Society of America, Research Triangle Park, NC. 1976 (Revised 1989). (ISBN: 1-55617-227-3)

ANSI/ISA-S5.5, *Graphic Symbols for Process Displays.* Instrument Society of America, Research Triangle Park, NC. 1985 (Approved 1986). (ISBN: 0-87664-935-5)

ANSI/ISA-S51.1, *Process Instrumentation Terminology.* Instrument Society of America, Research Triangle Park, NC. 1979. (ISBN: 0-87664-390-4)

Bibliography

Videotapes

Instrumentation Video Series. Instrument Society of America, Research Triangle Park, NC. 1985, 1986, 1987, 1988.

Continuous Process Control Series. Instrument Society of America, Research Triangle Park, NC. 1989.

Control Technology and Application Series. Instrument Society of America, Research Triangle Park, NC. 1988.

Industrial Measurement Series. Instrument Society of America, Research Triangle Park, NC. 1987.

INVOLVE™
**Interactive
Videodisc Instruction**

Controller Tuning Series.
Instrument Society of America, Research Triangle Park, NC. 1990.

Electronic Maintenance Series.
Instrument Society of America, Research Triangle Park, NC. 1991.

Fundamentals of Measurement Series.
Instrument Society of America, Research Triangle Park, NC. 1991.

Industrial Process Control Series.
Instrument Society of America, Research Triangle Park, NC. 1991.

Interpreting Process Control Diagrams.
Instrument Society of America, Research Triangle Park, NC. 1990.

Troubleshooting Series.
Instrument Society of America, Research Triangle Park, NC. 1990.

Index

C

Continuous control modes 7
Control mode 3

D

Derivative control 21

G

Gain 13

I

Integral control 18

O

Offset 17
Oscillation 5, 7, 16

P

PI control 19
PID control 20
Process loop 5
Proportional band 10, 13
Proportional control 7, 16
Proportional gain 11

R

Reset action 18

T

Two-position control 4, 5